FASHION

Exercise

BOOK

First published in the United Kingdom in 2014 by
Batsford
1 Gower Street
London WC1E 6HD

An imprint of Pavilion Books Group Ltd

Illustrations copyright © Frances Moffatt, 2014
Volume copyright © Batsford, 2014

ISBN: 9781849141365

A CIP catalogue record for this book is available from the British Library.

20 19 18 17 16 15
10 9 8 7 6 5 4 3

Repro by Mission, Hong Kong
Printed by GPS Group, Slovenia

This book can be ordered direct from the publisher at the website:
www.pavilionbooks.com, or try your local bookshop.

Frances Moffatt

FASHION

Exercise

BOOK

BATSFORD

INTRODUCTION

Dear Reader,

Welcome to the Fashion Exercise Book!

Fashion and illustration are two big passions in my life, and what I love most about fashion illustration is that you get to be a designer, stylist, hairdresser, make up artist, photographer and art director all rolled into one!

This book has been designed to inspire and guide all ages and abilities to unleash their creativity and produce their own beautiful fashion illustrations. Whether you are an aspiring fashion designer or illustrator, or someone who enjoys doodling and drawing but wants more guidance, the exercises in this book are designed to give you a 'jumping off' point. Be as uninhibited and inventive as possible when working your way through these pages, letting your imagination guide you.

So get your pencils, pens, paints, glue, and glitter out and have some fun!

Love Frances x

SPARKLING STILLETOS

Embellish these heels with glamourous gems

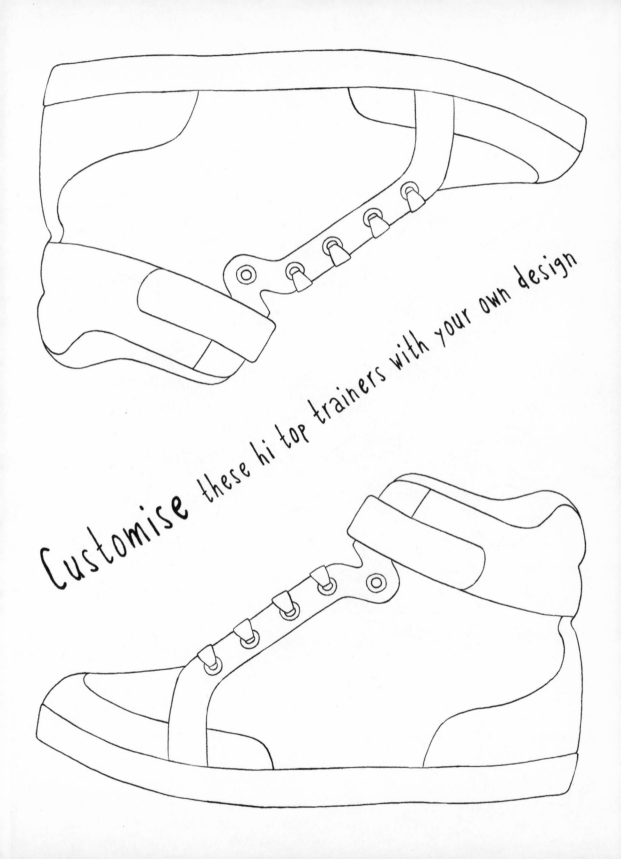

Customise these hi top trainers with your own design

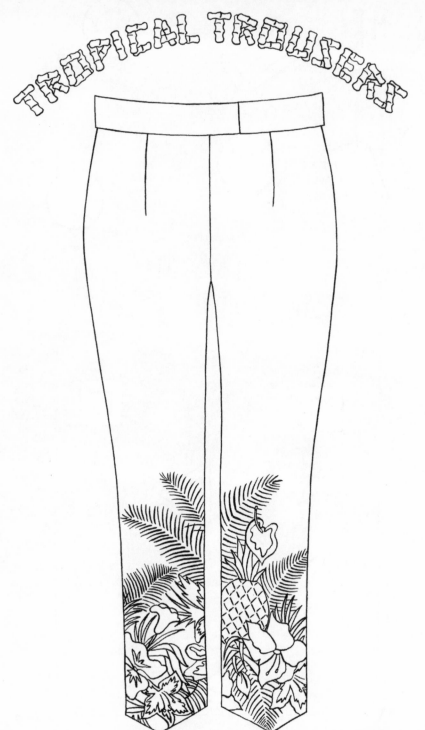

TROPICAL TROUSERS

Add to the foliage to create an all over pattern

CALL ME!

Design a stylish shell for this phone

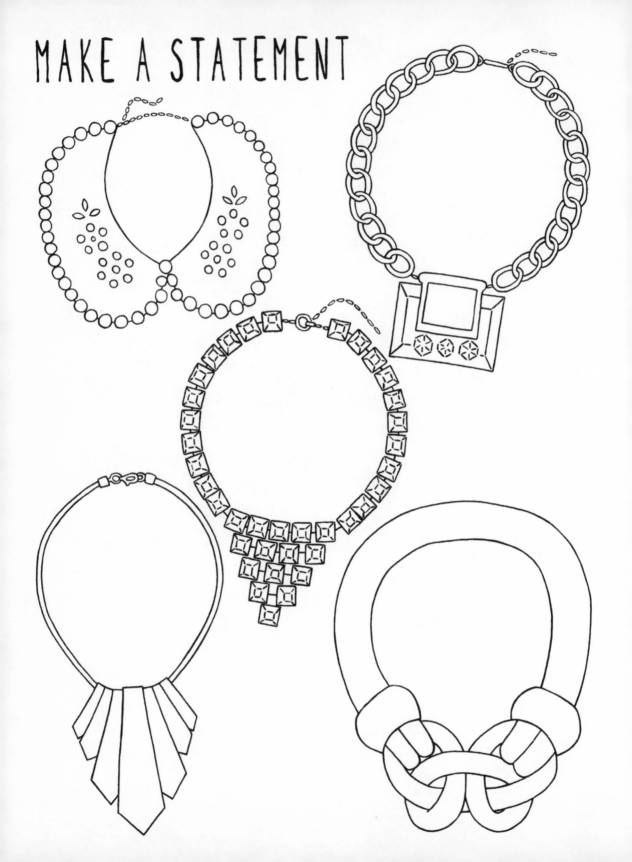

MAKE A STATEMENT

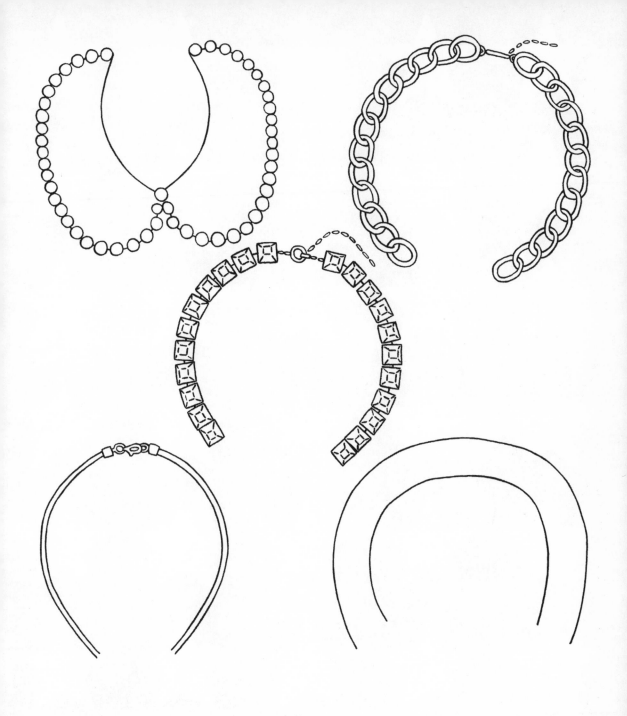

Design your own statement necklaces

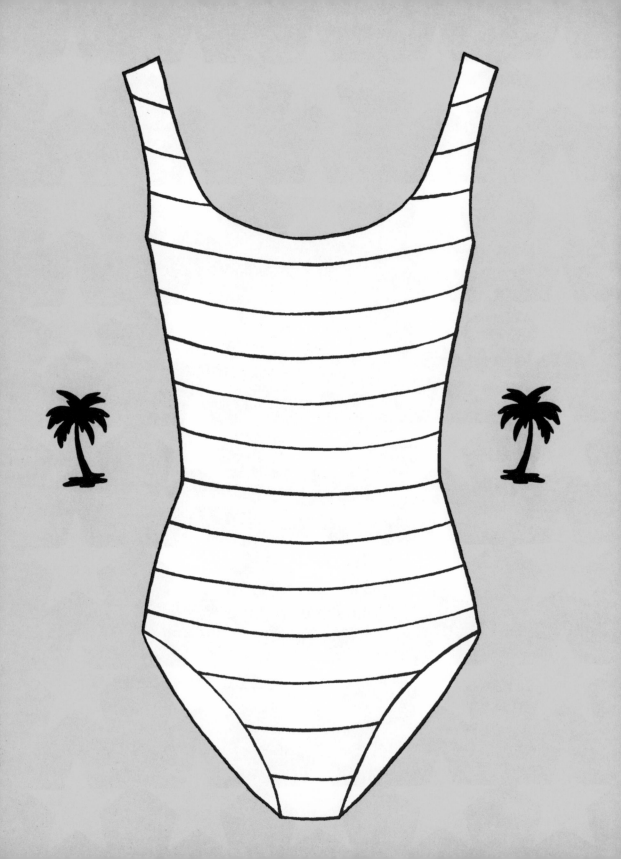

HEAVY METAL

Customise

this leather biker jacket

Why not draw a cool design on the back?

And how about some studs?

SWING TAG STYLE

BOUTIQUE

COOL KIMONO

Complete the floral design on this silk kimono

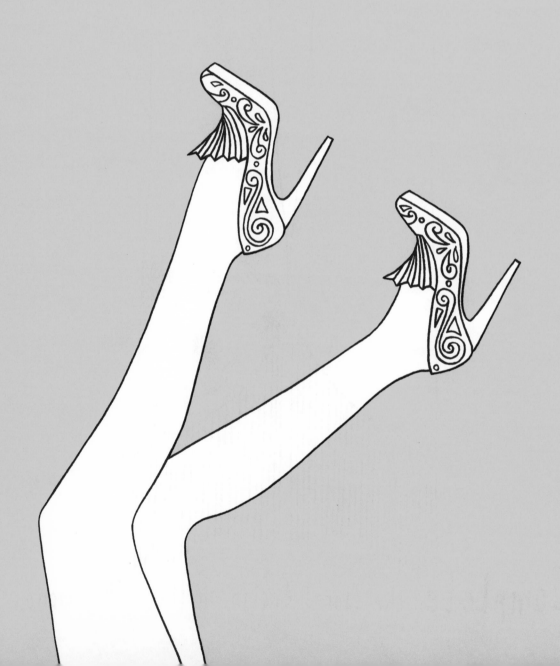

(DON'T BE A) BEAUTY SCHOOL DROPOUT !

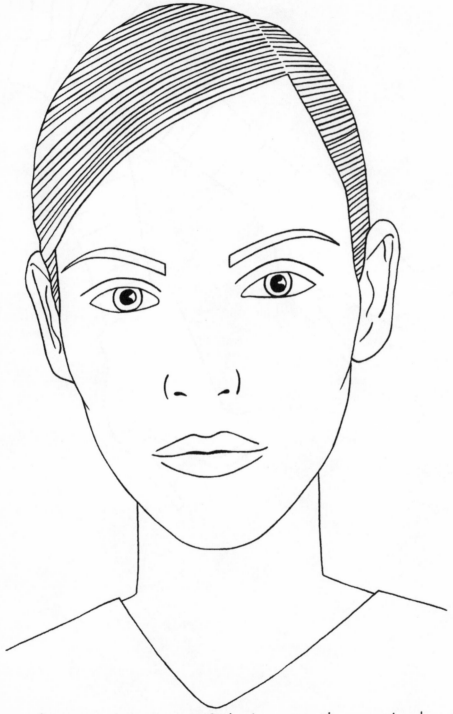

Create your own fabulous make up looks

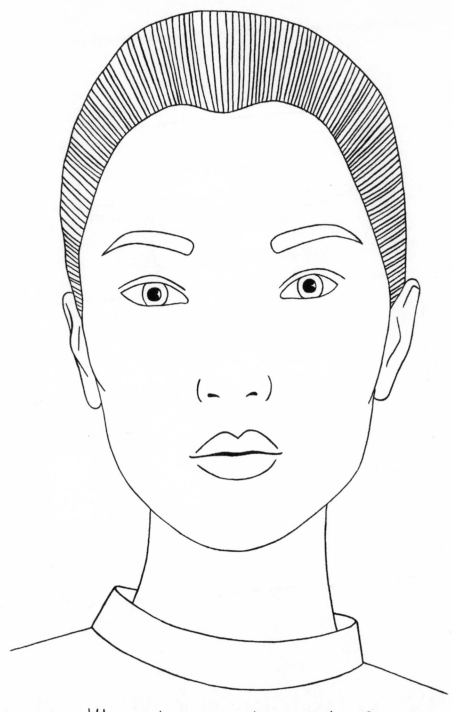

Why not use real cosmetics?

Draw the labels for these perfume bottles

STREET
STYLE
CITY OF CHIC

LONDON

MICKEY

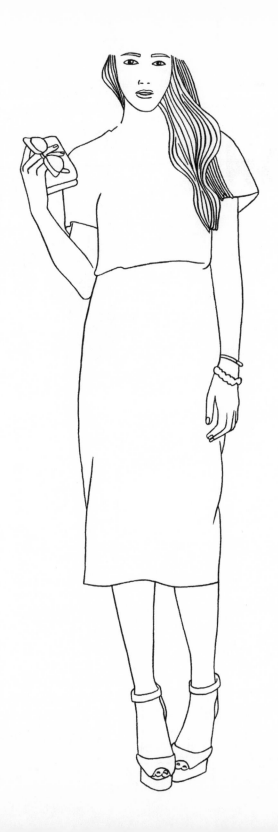

LONDON

TOTES AMAZE!

COOL

Decorate this bag with a cool design

HAND IN GLOVE 1

Create a design for the cuffs of this pair of gloves

FABULOUS
FOOTWEAR

A DAPPER DOG!

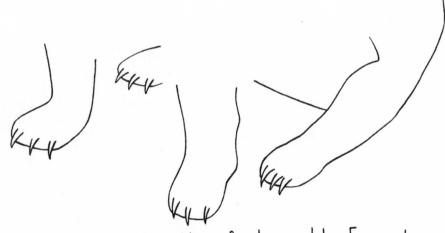

Design a jacket for this fashionable Frenchie

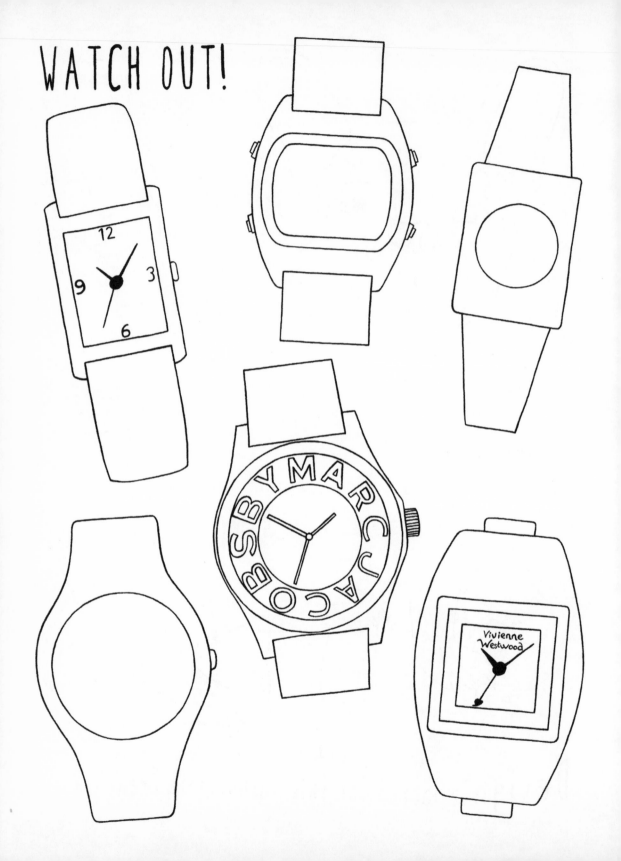

WATCH OUT!

Colour in these watches and design your own terrific timepieces

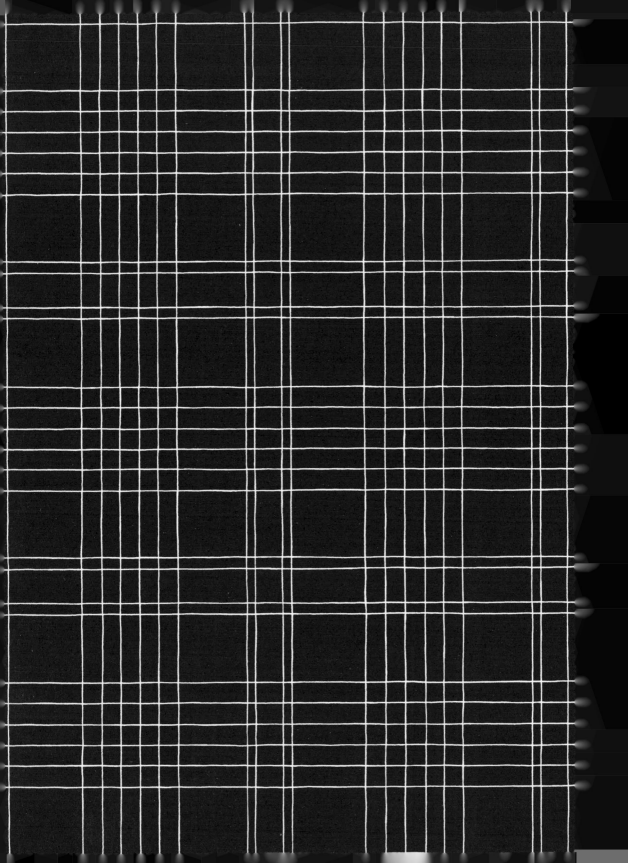

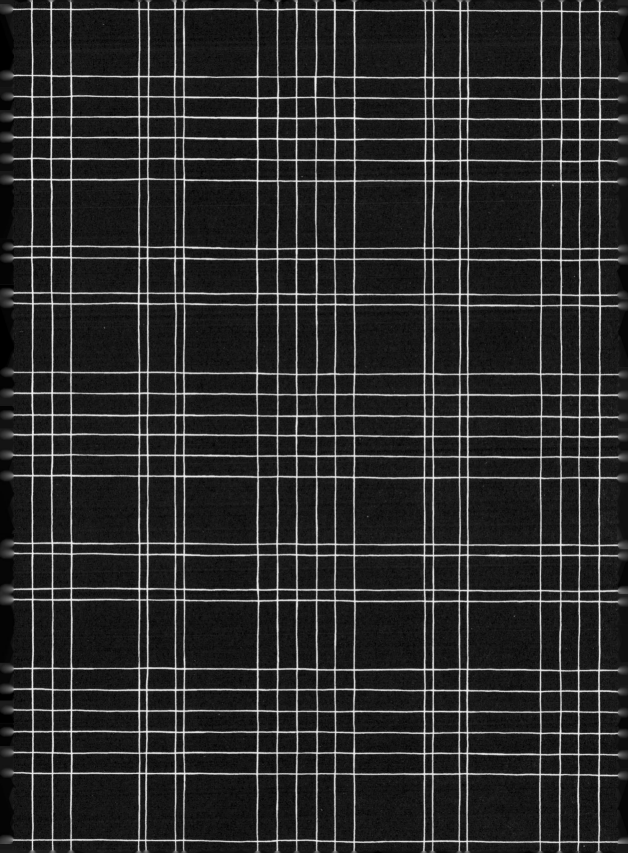

IT'S IN THE BAG

Think up some patterns for these bags

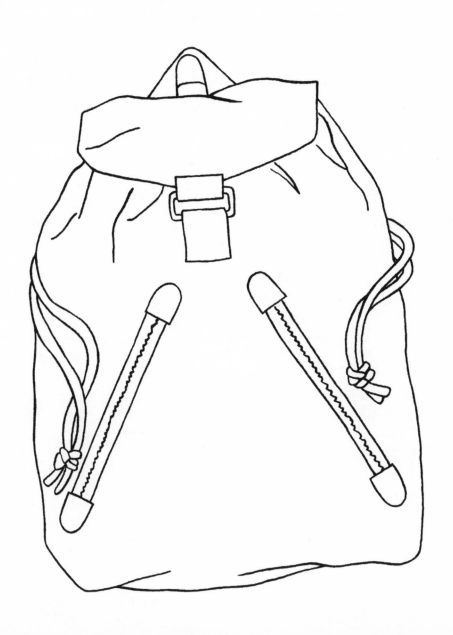

IN THE SHADE

JEEPERS PEEPERS

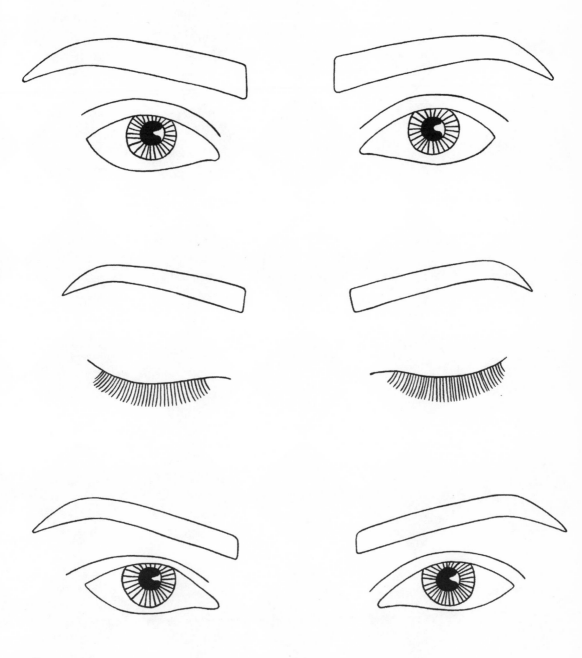

Design some cool make up looks for these eyes

PARIS

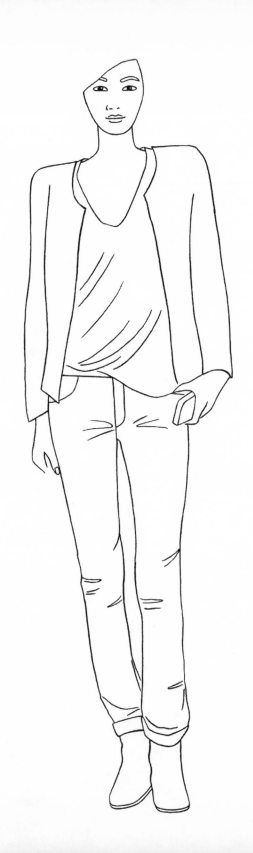

STREET
STYLE
CITY OF CHIC

PARIS

TRÈS CHIC

Design your own stylish silk scarf

CHOUPETTE

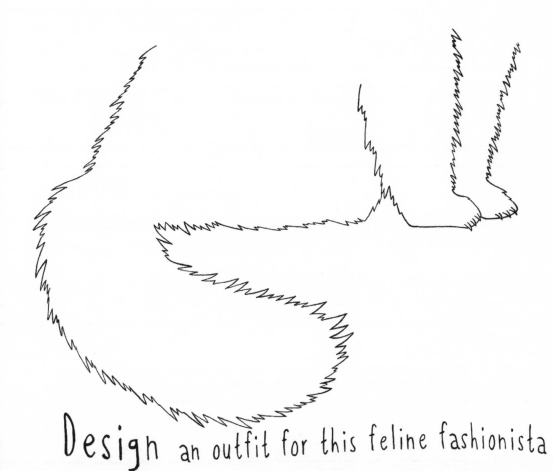

Design an outfit for this feline fashionista

BLINGING BEANIE

Complete the jewelled embellishment on this hat

TEA DRESS TIME

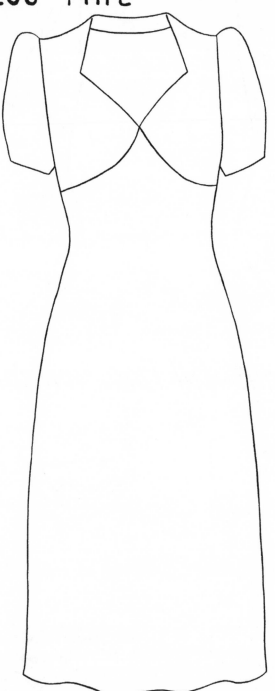

Design a floral pattern for this retro frock

Beautiful Beachwear

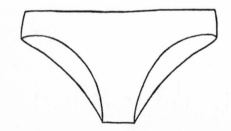

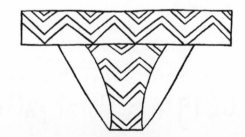

Design a bold pattern for this Fifties-style bikini

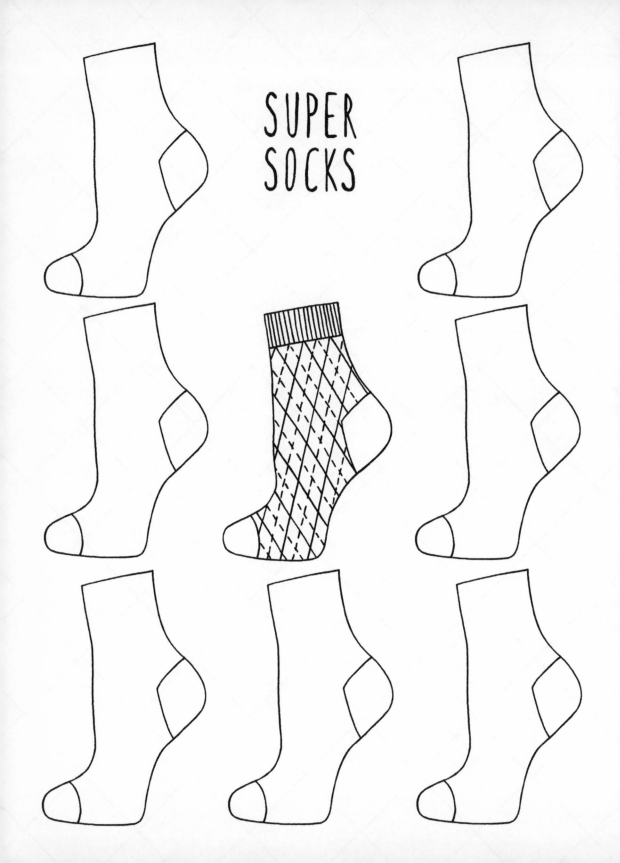

SUPER
SOCKS

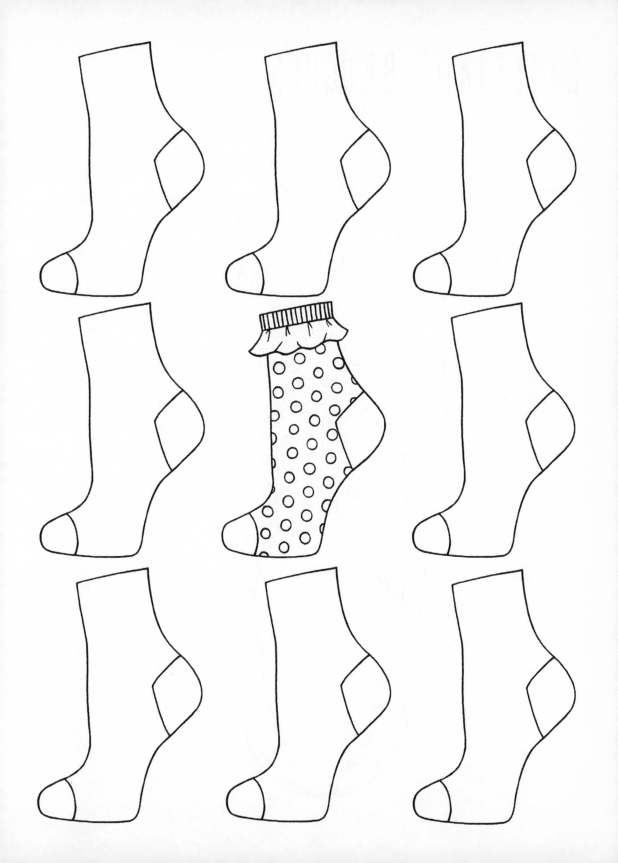

BRILLIANT BROGUES

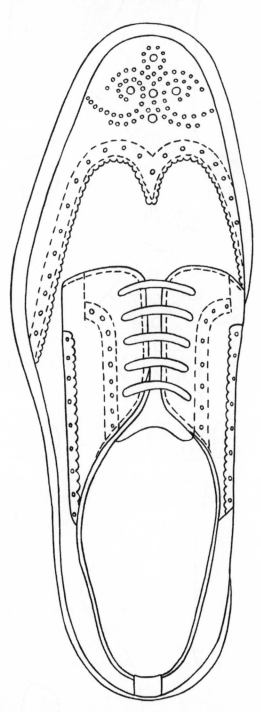

Complete the detailing

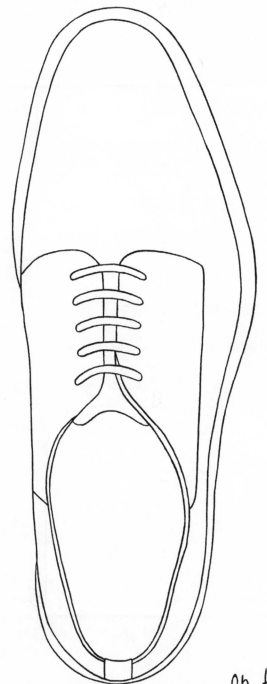

on this smart pair of shoes

PERFECT PURSES

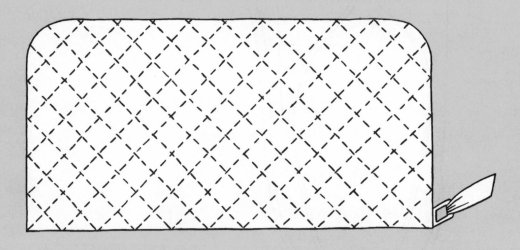

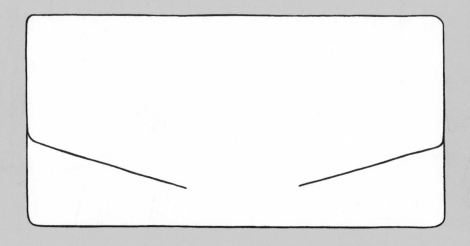

Design your own leather purse

GIG GUIDE

Draw your own rock concert style essentials

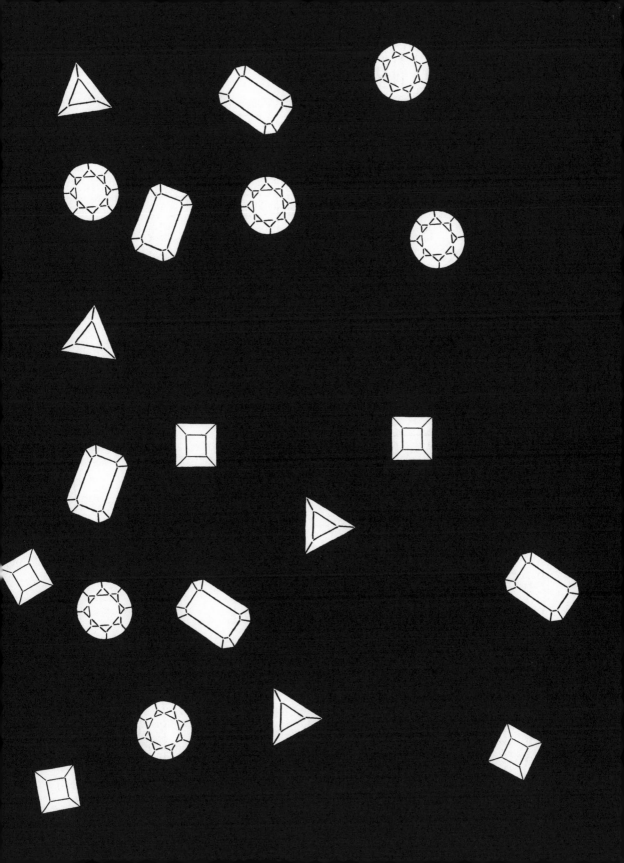

LOUD LEGGINGS

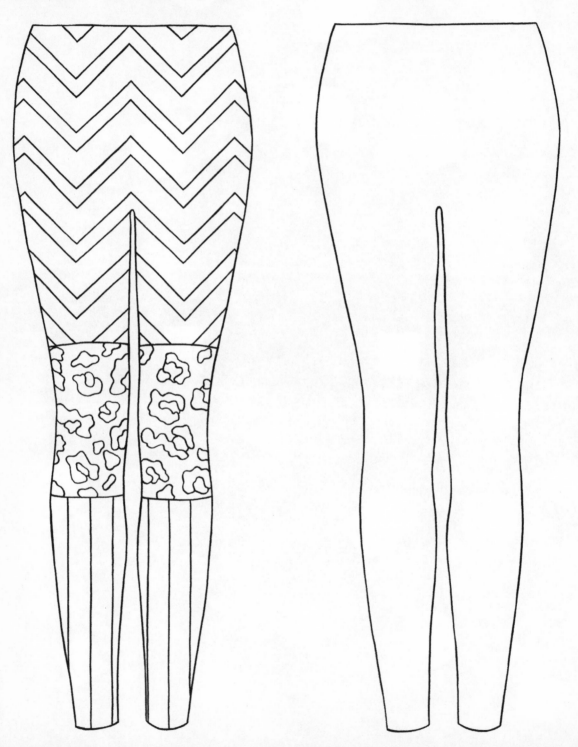

Design your own bold patterns for these leggings

FASHION
FASHION
FASHION
FASHION
FASHION
FASHION
FASHION
FASHION
FASHION
FASHION
FASHION
FASHION
FASHION

FASHION FASHION FASHION

FASHION FASHION

FASHION

FASHION

FASHION

FASHION FASHION

FASHION

FASHION

FASHION FASHION

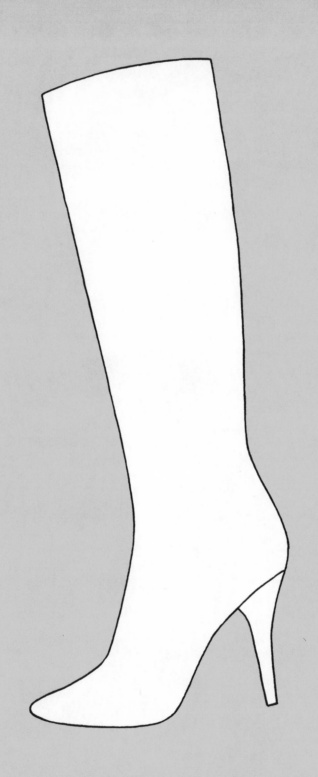

Make these shoes your own

VERA WANG
princess

Colour in
these bottles and design your own labels

YVES SAINT LAURENT

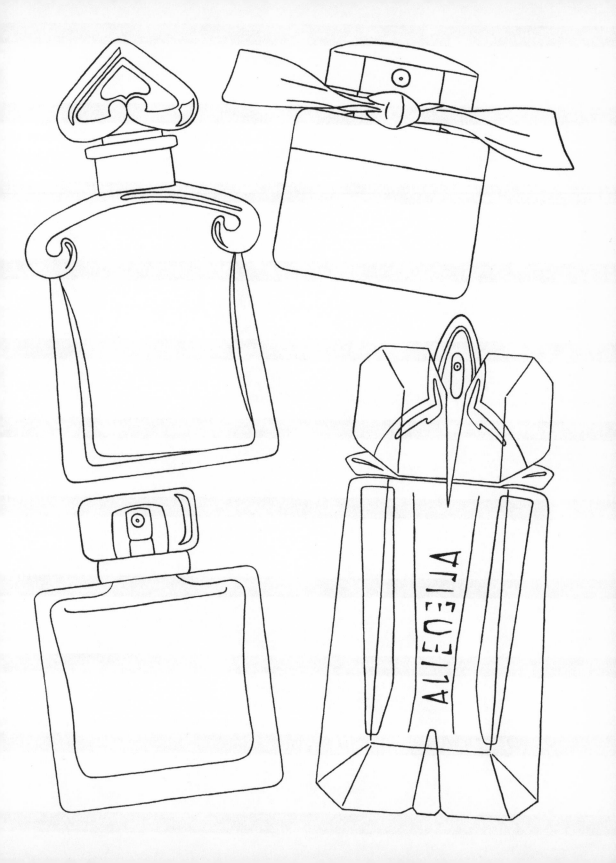

MARVELLOUS MILLINERY

Design your own fashionable hats

FESTIVAL FASHION

Draw your own festival style essentials

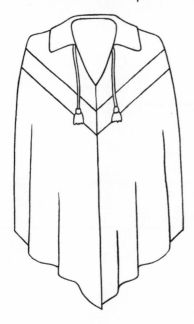

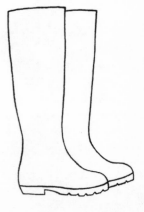

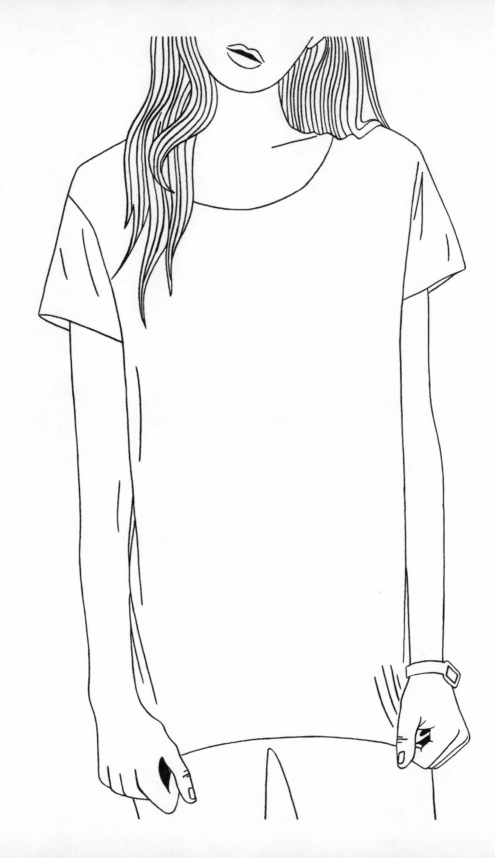

SLOGAN TEE STYLE

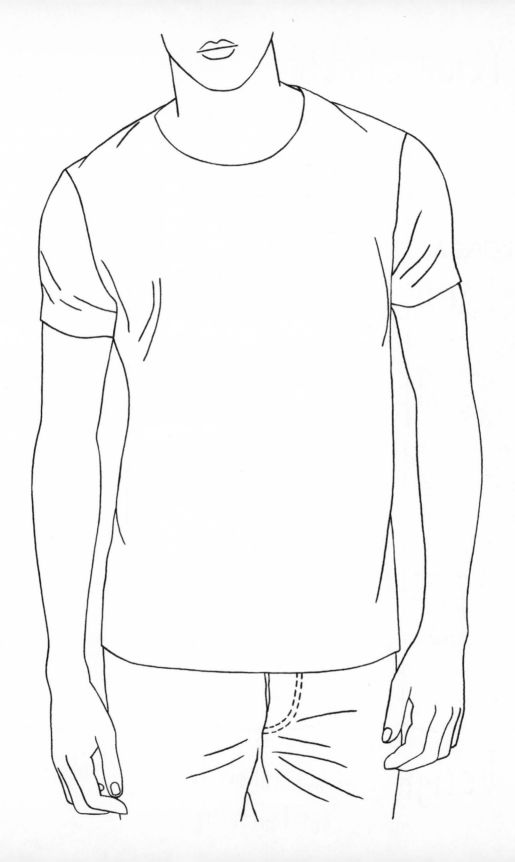

STYLISH STYLING

Design your own labels for these bottles of hairspray

SPARKLE!

Create a design for this top using real sequins

STREET
STYLE
CITY OF CHIC

MILAN

MILAN

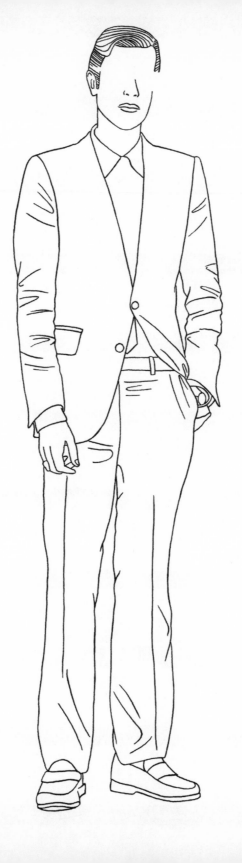

PERFECT POLISH

Fill these bottles with
beautiful nail varnish

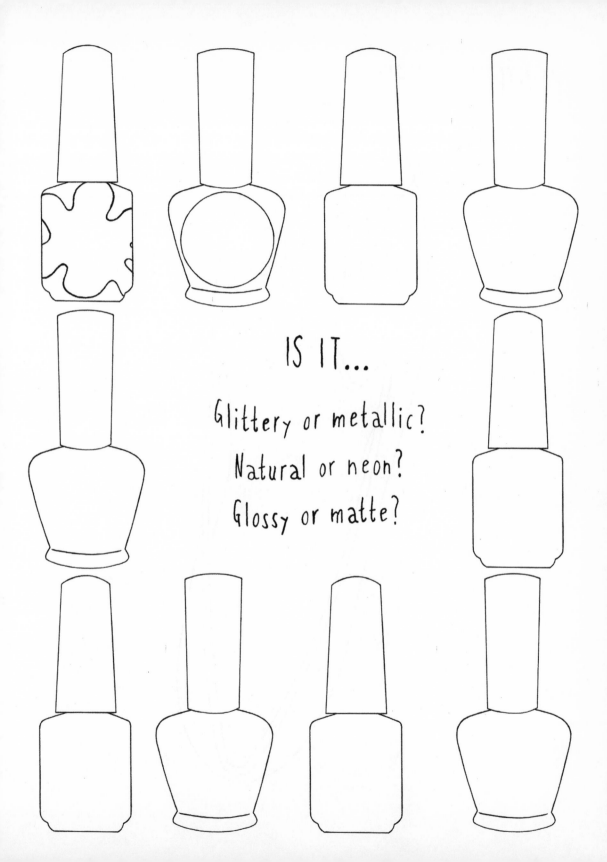

IS IT...

Glittery or metallic?
Natural or neon?
Glossy or matte?

PLAYFUL PUMPS

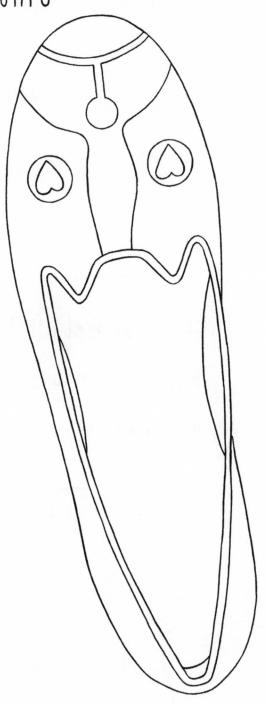

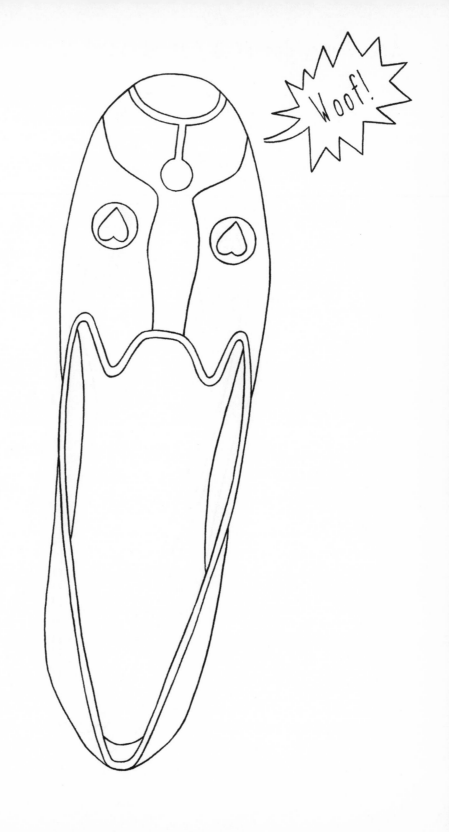

Are you a dog or a cat person?

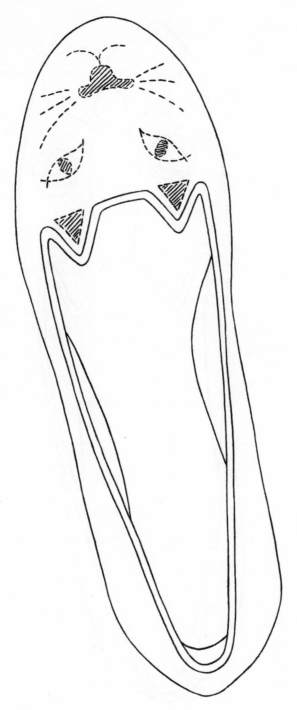

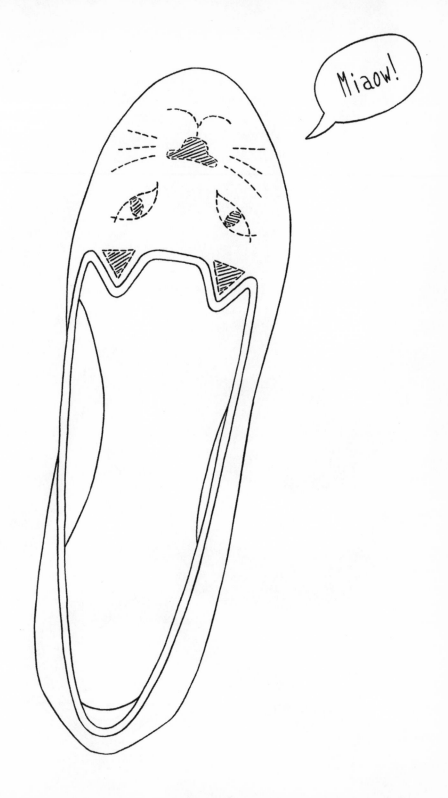

SHARP SHIRT

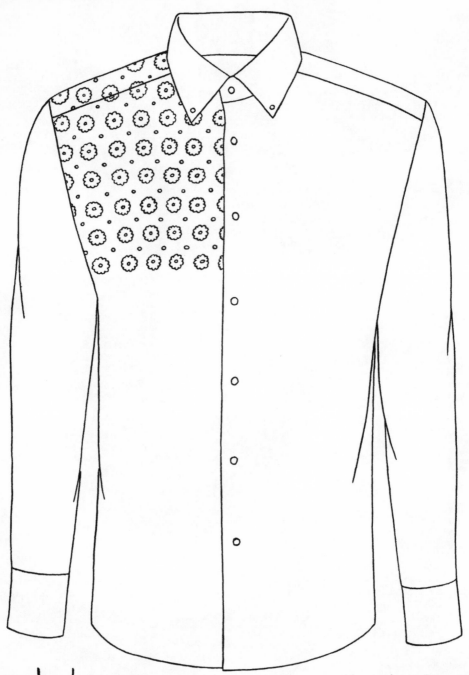

Complete the Liberty print on this button down

Colour in these **CREEPERS**

ANOTHER DAPPER DOG!

Design a coat and bow for this chic Chihuahua

LOVELY LIPSTICK

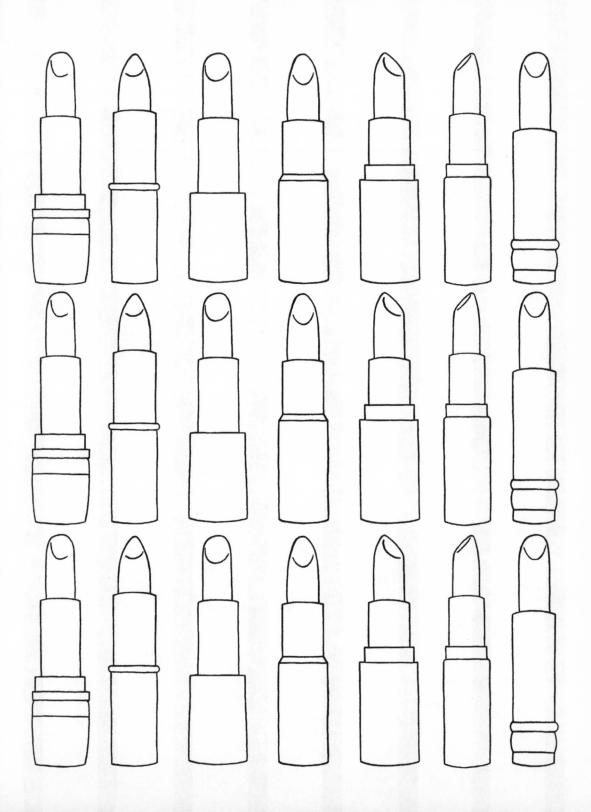

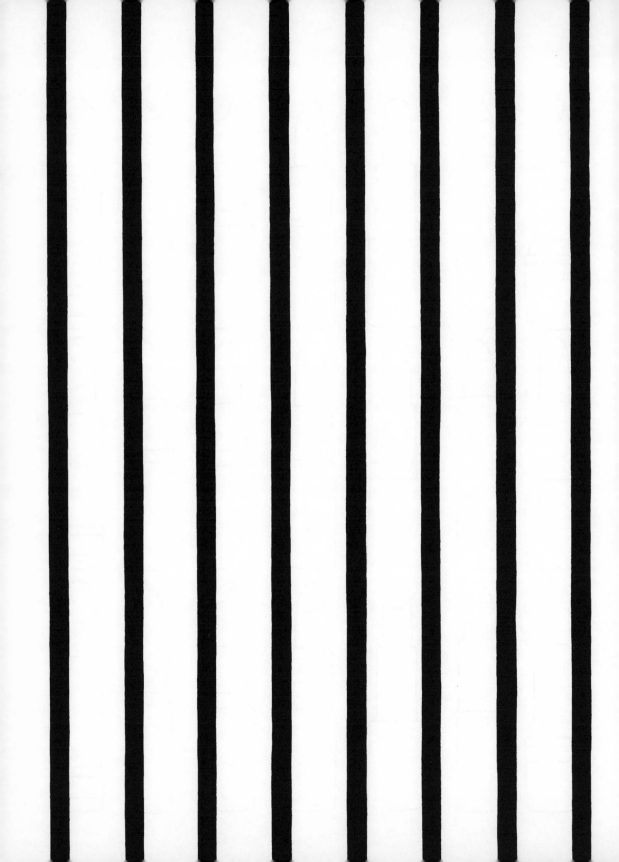

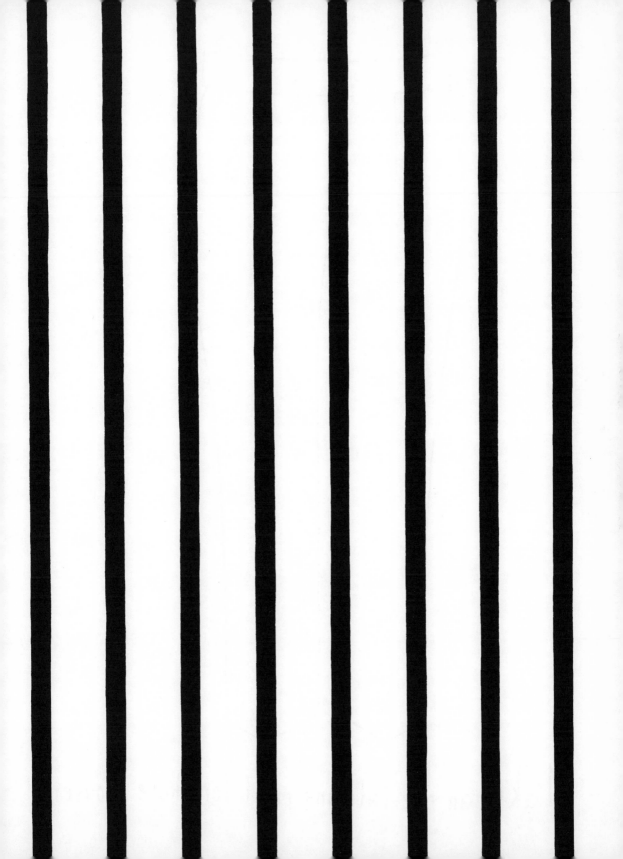

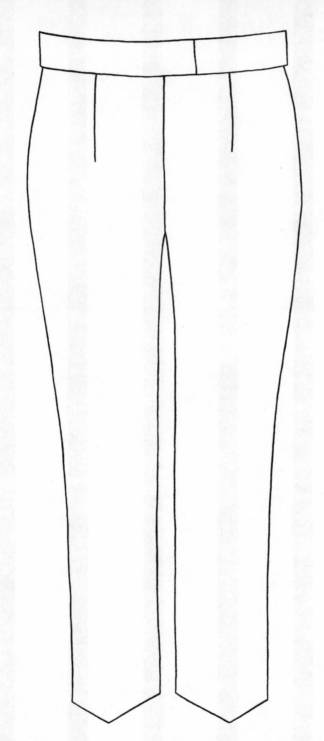

Make an eye-catching print for these trousers

BEAUTIFUL BELTS

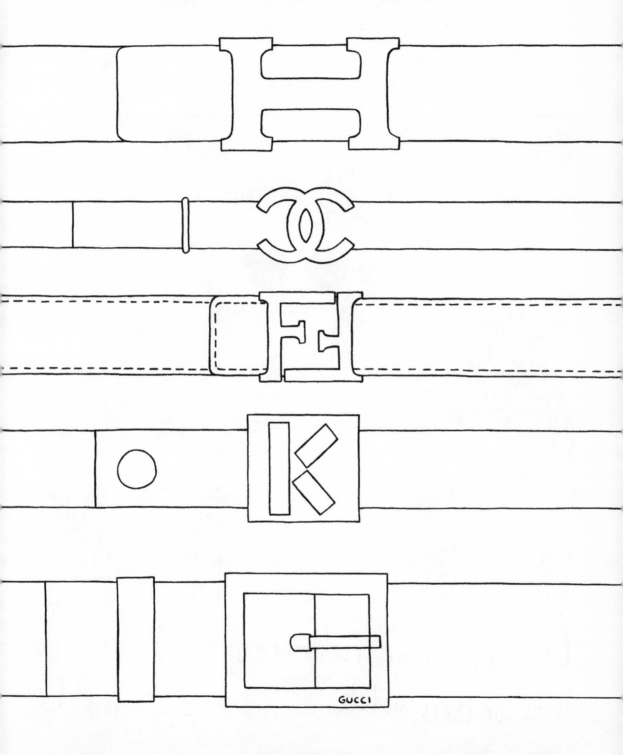

Create some fresh make up looks for these models

Now **design** your own hat, sunglasses and hairstyles

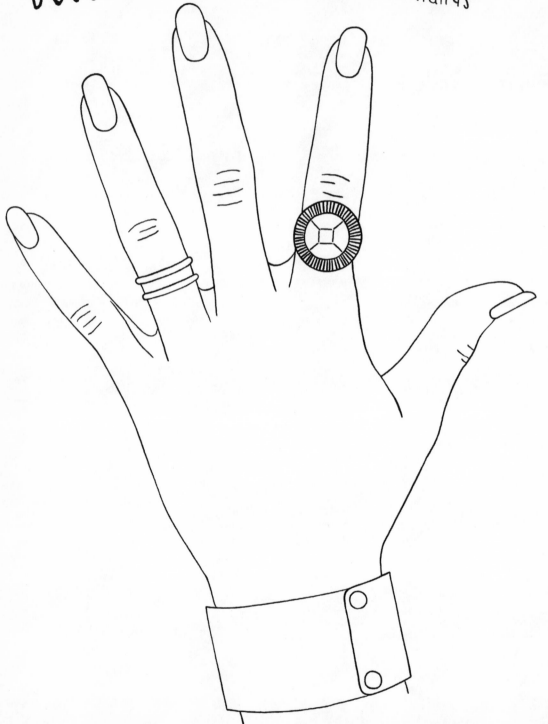

Decorate this handsome pair of hands

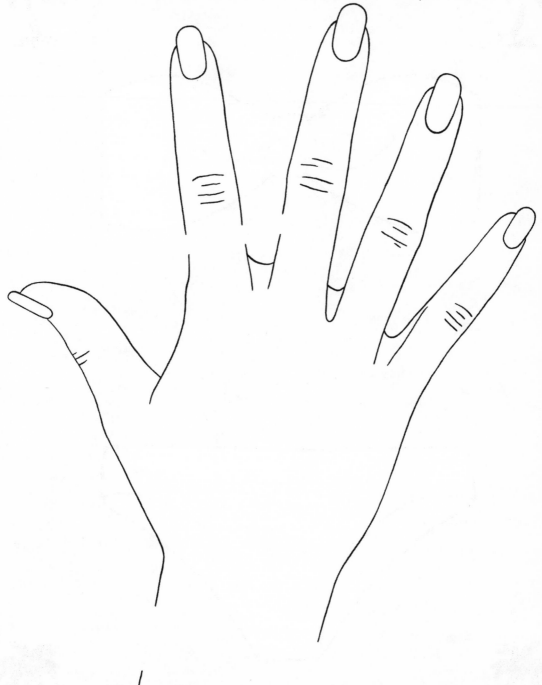

with nail art and jewellery

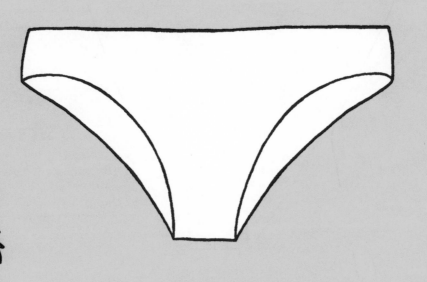

IT BAGS

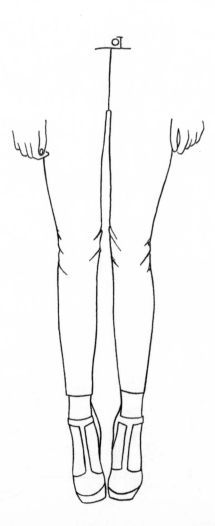

STREET
STYLE
CITY OF CHIC

NEW YORK

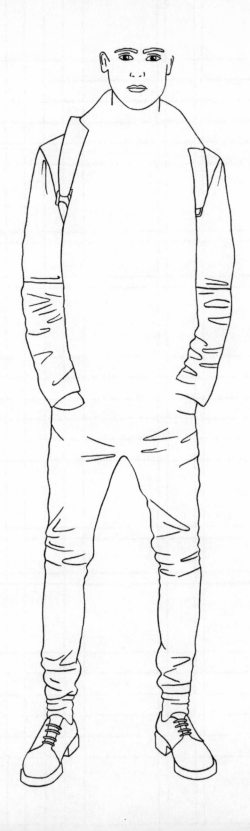

Frances' Fashion Blog

Profile:
Fashion blogging legend Susie Bubble!

Categories:

Street Style

Shop Reports

Catwalk

Profiles

Accessories

About Me

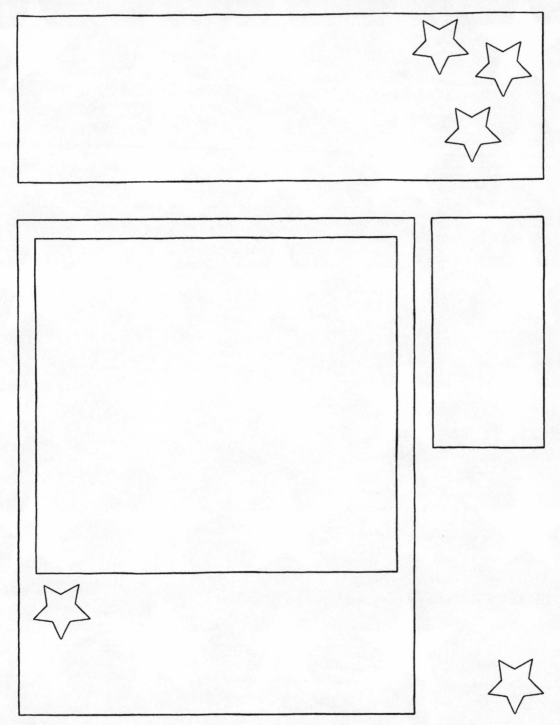

Design a front page for your own fashion blog

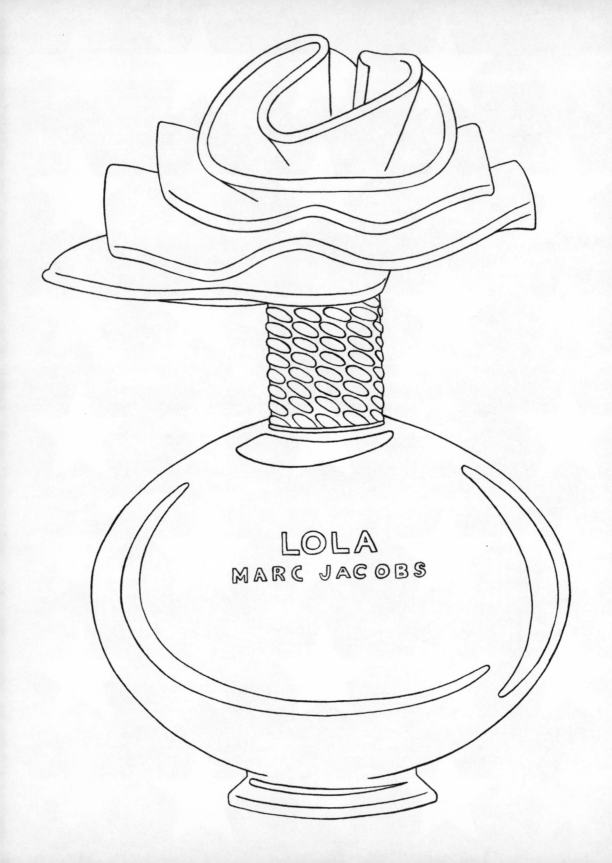

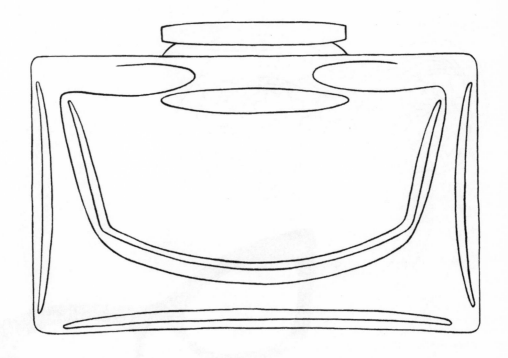

Draw a beautiful stopper for this bottle

Making eyes...

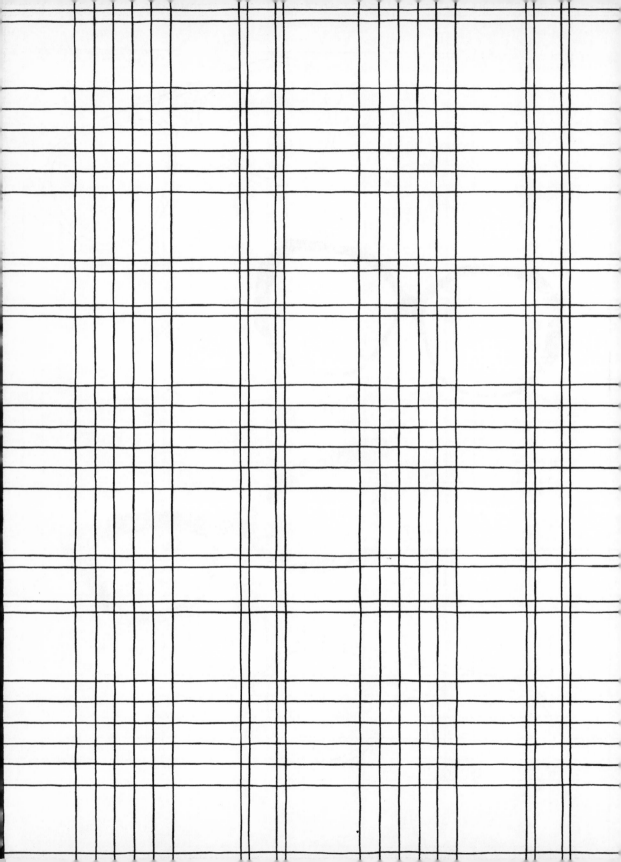

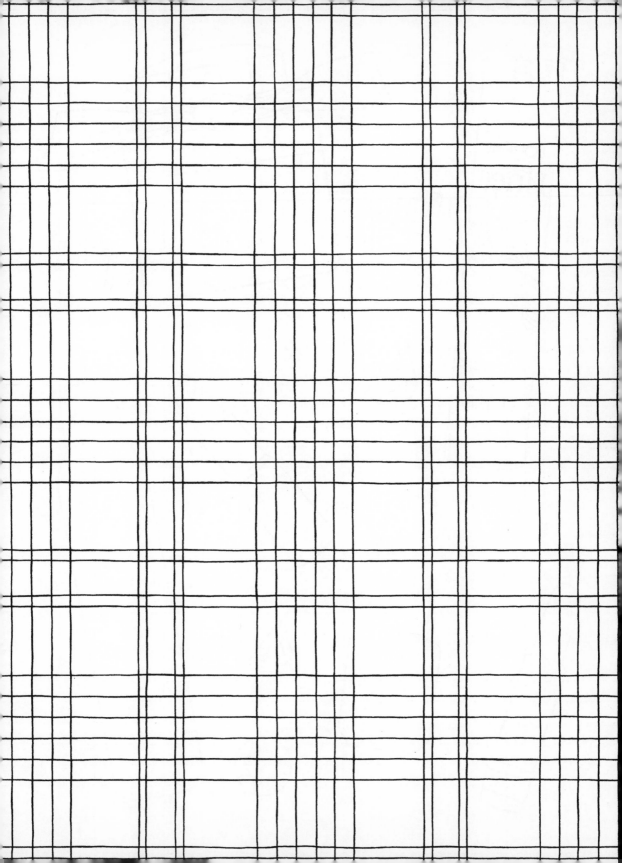

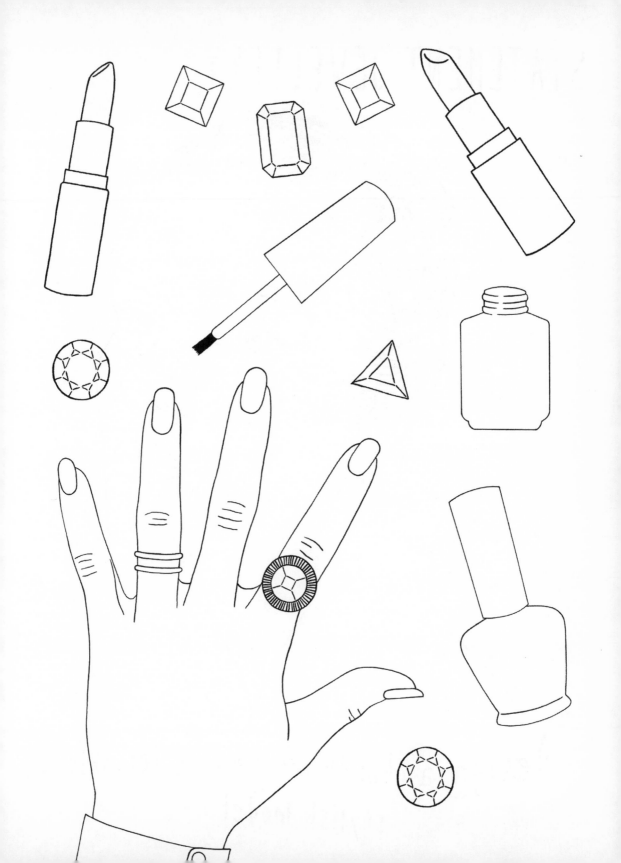

STATEMENT JEWELLERY

Design a chandelier earring for this stylish model

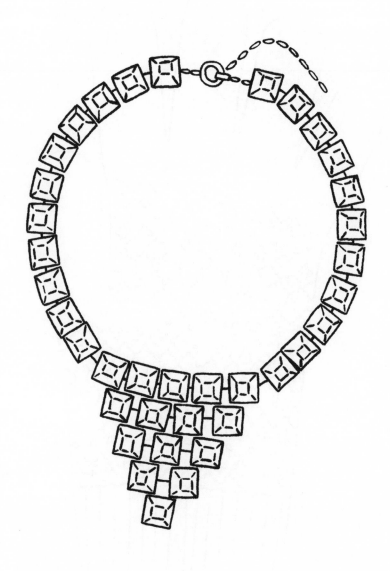

Add some colour to this bling!

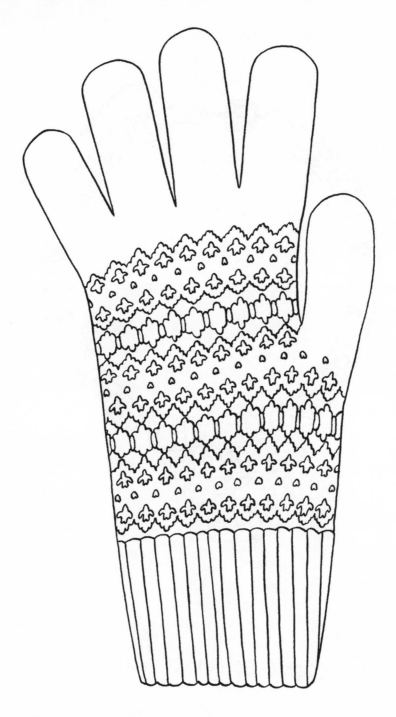

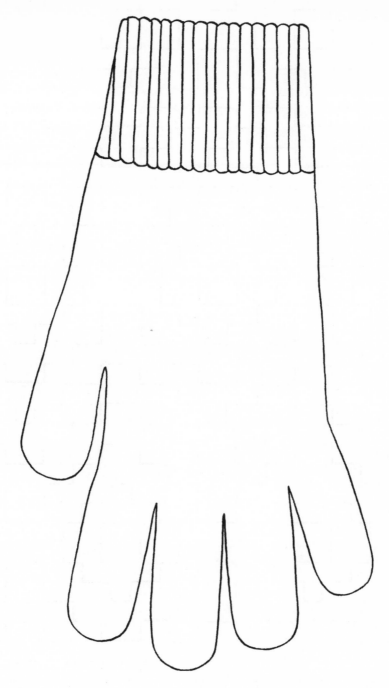

Complete the Fair Isle pattern on this pair of woolly gloves

#fashtag

Draw your own selfie...

Frances x

...and draw your friends

LEGS ELEVEN

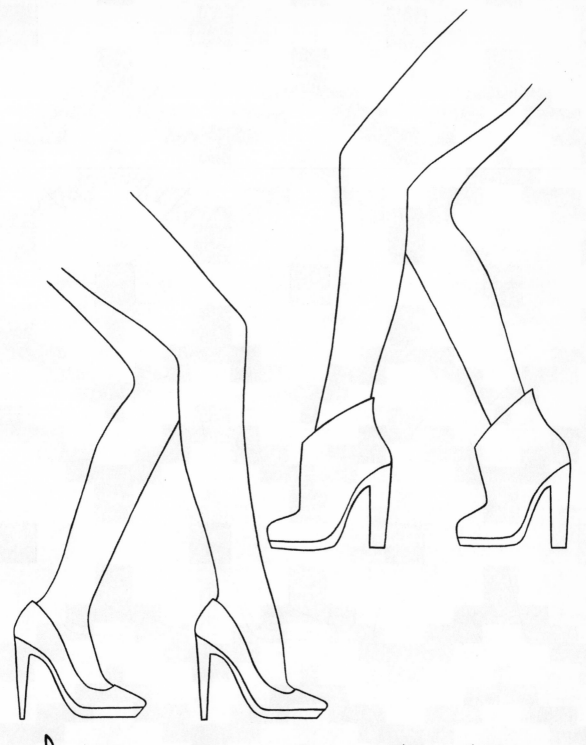

Design your own patterned tights and shoes

Style these models...

Add some colour and print